BUDDIE

Find all these Magical things inside...

Published 2020. Little Brother Books, Ground Floor, 23 Southernhay East, Exeter, Devon, EX1 1QL
Printed In Poland.
books@littlebrotherbooks.co.uk | www.littlebrotherbooks.co.uk
The Little Brother Books trademark, email and website addresses, are the sole and exclusive properties of Little Brother Books Limited.

elfontheshelf.com
® and © 2020 CCA and B, LLC. All Rights Reserved.

the ELF on the SHELF®

a Christmas tradition ™

THIS ANNUAL BELONGS TO

CUPAT

AND SCOUT ELF

BUDDIE

FIND US!

There is an elf hidden on every double page in this book. Can you find them all? Are there more girl elves or boy elves hiding? Write your answers in the boxes.

Christmas is coming... Turn the page to start the festive fun...

Introducing the

SCOUT ELVES

As the only elves that interact with humans, Santa's Scout Elves have an important job to do. Read on to find out more about their magical role.

Magical Moment

When a Scout Elf is adopted by a family the family chooses their name. This is a very special moment as it's when the elf's Christmas magic is activated. This gives elves the power they need to zip to the North Pole and back as fast as lightning.

Keeping Watch

In the run up to Christmas, an elf watches their family's adventures during the day. At night they fly back to the North Pole to report kind deeds to Santa. By the time the family wakes up in the morning, their elf is back in the house waiting in a new hiding place.

Tips and Tricks

Scout Elves are specially trained in the North Pole by the Scout Elf Training Team, where they learn to run fast, jump safely and climb high. They're also given the latest tips to help them create innovative hiding spots in their family's home.

North Pole Fun

Scout Elves love to have fun, both in their family's home and at the North Pole. Each night, before they head back to their families, elves enjoy meeting up to play in the snow, toast marshmallows over a campfire or play their favourite sport.

A Day in the Life of a Scout Elf...

Read Buddy's diary to find out what Scout Elves get up to on a typical December day.

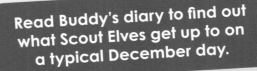

7AM: From my new hiding spot, I hear the first family member start to stir. Today, I'm hanging upside down from the top of the Christmas tree so I'll need to use all my special training to stay still!

7.30AM: The children are the first ones downstairs. It takes them a few minutes to find me and they're very excited when they do!

10AM: The family are making Christmas cards for friends with nice messages inside. I'll report this kind deed back to Santa later.

3PM: The family leave the house to go Christmas shopping but I still don't move as I don't know when they'll be back. A Scout Elf must always stay alert!

6PM: Over dinner, the family chat about their day. There are so many kind things I can tell Santa about.

10PM: Everyone is fast asleep so I quietly leave the house and use my magic to fly back to the North Pole.

10.30PM: It's my turn to see Santa and report back to him. He's very pleased with my family's kind deeds today. They will definitely be on his nice list!

11PM: It's time to catch up with my friends and play in the snow. After a game of football we enjoy a warming cup of hot chocolate – delicious!

4AM: Time to fly back to my family.

5.30AM: I've set up my new hiding spot using some props my family helpfully left out for me. I can't wait to see them again in the morning.

SPECIAL DELIVERY

Presents arrive at Santa's Shipping Yard on a special slide.
Help the elves get this present from the slide to the cart,
avoiding the obstacles along the way.

PULL

START

FINISH

Answers on pages 76-77

9

Magical Names

When a Scout Elf is named by their family they get their Christmas magic. Here are some ideas to help you choose the perfect name for your North Pole pal.

Festive Inspiration

Inspiration is all around you at Christmas time so why not choose a festive name for your North Pole visitor? You could name them after a decoration, a sweet treat or a favourite song. Bauble, Truffle or Frosty anyone?

UNIQUE NAME

Give your elf a one-of-a-kind name by choosing something unusual. You could create a unique name by rearranging the letters in your family members' names or blending two words together.

POT LUCK

Why not let luck decide your elf's new name? As a family, brainstorm as many name ideas as you can. Choose your favourite 10, put them into a hat and pick one out.

TOP 20 ELF NAMES

1. Buddie
2. Snowflake
3. Elfie
4. Jingle
5. Jingles
6. Sparkle
7. Peppermint
8. Jack
9. Holly
10. Chippie
11. Charlie
12. Fred
13. Twinkle
14. Max
15. Elfy
16. Sparkles
17. Elvis
18. Ginger
19. Tinsel
20. Jolly

TEAM EFFORT

Finding it hard to agree on a name? Then give your elf all the names instead! Each family member chooses their favourite, then you put them together to create a first name, middle names and a surname.

Perfect Fit

Choose a name that suits your elf's personality. Are they cheeky, creative, funny or adventurous? If you're not sure yet, base your elf's name on words that describe your family.

Elf Outfits

Design an outfit for your Scout Elf by choosing your favourite items from the clothes and accessories below. Make them look fabYULEous!

Scout Elf SUPER HERO

JINGLE BELLS ROCK!

CHRISTMAS ROCKS!

DON'T FORGET TO ADD SOME ELF ACCESSORIES!

13

SHARING letter to

WARNING!
ADULT GUIDANCE IS
NEEDED FOR THIS ACTIVITY.

SANTA

Santa loves reading letters from children all over the world. You can write your own letter on the page opposite and send it to the man himself!

Tell Santa about some of the kind things you've been doing.

FESTIVE FUNNY!

Write your favourite festive joke for Santa here.

MY KIND DEEDS

Q:

....

....

A:

POSTING YOUR LETTER

Make sure you've read **page 13** before you cut out each piece.

If you don't want to cut up your book, photocopy or scan and print this page instead.

Once you've written your letter to Santa, your list of kind deeds and your Christmas joke, cut everything out, pop it all in an envelope, stick on a stamp and send it to the address below. This is the Southern Branch of the North Pole and is filled with humans who work for Santa. They will happily pass on your letter.

DID YOU KNOW?

Santa's favourite joke is:

Q: What do you call an elf who sings?

A: A wrapper!

Santa
Santa's Grotto
Reindeerland
XM4 5HQ

Dear Santa

My name is ....

and I can't wait until Christmas!

My Scout Elf is called ....

and they have been watching all the kind

things my family and I have been doing.

This Christmas, on my wish list is ....

....

I'll leave a treat of ....

for you and the reindeer on Christmas Eve.

I hope you have fun in the North Pole

getting ready for the big day!

 love from ....

Meet the Elf Pets®

These special animals have a very important job to do. Read on to find out more about Santa's furry friends.

SANTA'S HELPERS

As well as Santa and his Scout Elves, the North Pole is home to some very important animals, the Elf Pets®. These trusted companions help Santa make Christmas special for children all around the world.

CHRISTMAS CHEER

To help him travel around the world on Christmas Eve, Santa uses Christmas magic which is made from Christmas cheer. It's the job of the Elf Pets® to collect Christmas cheer which is created when children do kind things.

Elf Pets®
Saint Bernard

Each pup has a magical barrel around their neck, decorated with a golden heart. When children are kind and create Christmas cheer, the pup collects and stores it inside the barrel.

Elf Pets®
Reindeer

Christmas spirit is what Santa needs to make his sleigh soar on Christmas Eve! Christmas spirit is stored in the reindeer's golden heart charm and is created by children snuggling and hugging their pet all season long.

Elf Pets®
Arctic Fox

The snowy white cubs wear a snow globe around their neck. Children can shake it to show Santa they believe. On Christmas Eve, the cubs shake their tails to create the Northern Lights which shield Santa's sleigh.

DID YOU KNOW?

Each Saint Bernard pup has a special heart-shaped mark on their right ear.

FAB**YULE**OUS FUN!

Can you crack the code to reveal some of the Scout Elves' favourite sayings? They're so Elf-dorable!

KEY

A	B	C	D	E	F	G	H	I	J	K	L	M
N	O	P	Q	R	S	T	U	V	W	X	Y	Z

1

S N O W ___ ___ ___ ___ B ___ ___ ___ ___ ,

___ ___ ___ ___ ___ ___ ___ ___ ___ ___ ___ !

2.

_ _ _ _

_ _ _ _ _ _ _ !

3.

W E R U N O N

CHRISTMAS SPIRIt !

4.

_ _ _ _ _ ,

_ _ _ _ _ _ _ !

Answers on pages 76-77

19

Guide to the
NORTH POLE

With a bustling city centre, lamp post-lined streets and swirling snow, the North Pole is a magical place. Let's find out more about Santa's wintry home.

TOP SECRET INFO

There's a room in the North Pole lined with row upon row of bookshelves where you can learn everything there is to know about Christmas. How does Santa's sleigh fly? How is Christmas magic made? What elements make up Christmas Spirit? The answers to these and other questions lie within the walls of this top secret room.

DID YOU KNOW?

When Santa has an important announcement to make he gathers all the elves in the North Pole's City Centre.

SWEET TREATS

Scout Elves love sweet treats so the North Pole Sweet Shop is always busy. Here elves can sample delicious cookies, cakes, pies and pastries and choose from one of 25 different flavours of hot chocolate. The shop is run by Mrs. Claus who bakes each mouth-watering treat herself.

LOTS OF LETTERS

Santa receives millions of letters every year and they all end up in Santa's Grotto. It's a busy and bustling place filled with bulging mail sacks and sky-high piles of letters. The Scout Elves who work there sort and store the letters and make sure that Santa reads every single one.

Festive FASHION

Did you know that the Scout Elves' distinctive red and white uniform was designed by Mrs. Claus herself? Deep in the middle of the North Pole you'll find her studio crammed full of fashionable fabrics and design ideas. Here she creates a new line of elf clothing every season.

CHRISTMAS CLOSE-UPS

The Scout Elves love absolutely everything about Christmas! Can you work out which festive things are shown in the close-ups below?

1

2

3

4

5

6

Answers on pages 76-77

Let's be Jolly!

Scout Elves are always jolly, especially at Christmas time. Join the dots to make this elf jump for joy!

Now colour in your picture!

Winter Wishes

Spread the Scout Elf joy by sending these magical Christmas cards to someone you love.

YOU WILL NEED

- Scissors
- Glue
- Glitter

WARNING!
ADULT GUIDANCE IS NEEDED FOR THIS ACTIVITY.

HOW TO MAKE

1. Ask an adult to help you cut out both cards along the dotted lines.

2. Add a bit of Scout Elf sparkle by decorating your cards with glitter.

3. Fold both cards in half down the middle.

4. Write your cards, pop them in envelopes and deliver them to your friends or family.

Don't forget to wish your Scout Elf a merry Christmas! Why not make an elf-sized card and leave it out for them to find?

'Tis the season
to sparkle!

Have your Elf
a merry Christmas!

JOLLY JOKES

Make your friends chuckle with some of the Scout Elves' favourite festive funnies.

Q: What do you call a snowman in the summer?

A: A puddle!

FUNNY RATING

Q: Why did the elf put her bed in the fireplace?

A: She wanted to sleep like a log!

FUNNY RATING

Q: What do you call Santa when he stops moving?

A: Santa Pause!

FUNNY RATING

Q: What do snowmen do at the weekend?

A: Chill out!

FUNNY RATING

Q: What should you give your parents at Christmas?

A: A list of what you want!

FUNNY RATING

Q: What goes 'Oh, oh, oh'?

A: Santa walking backwards!

FUNNY RATING

LAUGH-O-METER

1 2 3 4 5

Give each jolly joke a funny rating out of 5.

NORTH POLE ROLE

Everyone in the North Pole works hard to make Christmas magical. If you lived there, what important job would Santa give you? Answer these questions to find out.

1

What birthday present would you give a friend?

A A stuffed animal
B Theme park tickets
C A homemade cake

2

What do you want to be when you grow up?

A A vet
B A personal trainer
C A chef

4

What do you like to do at the weekend?

A Play with pets
B Work on a project
C Make something

5

What's your favourite snack?

A Crunchy veg sticks
B A filling sandwich
C A sweet treat

3

How would your friends describe you?

- Ⓐ Kind
- Ⓑ Adventurous
- Ⓒ Creative

6

What would you find most relaxing?

- Ⓐ Stroking a cat
- Ⓑ Running around outside
- Ⓒ Making something in the kitchen

Mostly Ⓐs
REINDEER STABLE HAND

You're kind, caring and love animals. Looking after Santa's four-legged friends would be your dream North Pole job. When can you start?

Mostly Ⓑs
SCOUT ELF TRAINER

You adore adventure and have lots of energy so working as a Scout Elf Trainer would suit you to the ground. Your trainees would learn so much from you.

Mostly Ⓒs
COOKIE BAKER

Your sweet tooth and creativity would make you the perfect North Pole Cookie Baker. You and Mrs. Claus would have so much fun making treats for everyone.

Reindeer Food

Make this delicious treat to leave for Santa's helpers on Christmas Eve. You'll be pleased to know it isn't just for reindeers – children can eat it too!

YOU WILL NEED

- 150g cornflakes
- 115g butter
- 75g sugar sprinkles
- Small food bags
- Ribbon
- Scissors
- Hole punch

How to make

1. Put the cornflakes in a bowl.

2. Melt the butter in a microwave and pour it over the cornflakes.

3. Add the sprinkles to the bowl and stir well until the cornflakes are coated in butter and sprinkles.

4. Leave the reindeer food to cool completely

The Finishing Touch

1. Package the reindeer food into clear bags.

2. Cut out the labels below and punch a hole in each one where the circle is.

3. Cut a 10cm length of ribbon for each bag.

4. Thread a piece of ribbon through the hole in the label, then use the ribbon to tie the bag closed.

5. Repeat this step for each bag.

So Elf-dorable!

DID YOU KNOW?

This top secret recipe has come straight from the North Pole by permission of Mrs. Claus.

Reindeer Food
Sprinkle outside for Santa's Reindeer.

Reindeer Food
Sprinkle outside for Santa's Reindeer.

Reindeer Food
Sprinkle outside for Santa's Reindeer.

Reindeer Food
Sprinkle outside for Santa's Reindeer.

FUN FACTS

The Scout Elves' home is a fascinating place. Read on to discover some cool facts from the chilly North Pole.

2 Scout Elves eat over 10 million chocolate chip cookies each year.

1

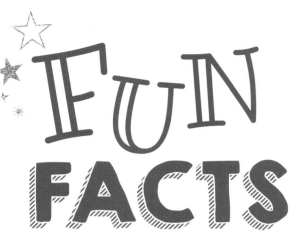

On Christmas Eve, Elf Pets® Reindeer grow to full size to guide Santa's sleigh.

3 Mrs. Claus can make at least 25 different flavours of hot chocolate.

4 The oldest person to ever send a letter to Santa was 92.

5

60% of children include a drawing with their letter to Santa.

NORTH POLE

6

Santa's birthday is on March 15th.

7

Elf Pets® Artic Fox cubs create the Northern Lights which help Santa fly around the world on Christmas Eve without being seen.

8

Santa receives more than 5 million letters each Christmas – and he reads every single one.

10

Santa's Scout Elf Training Team teaches elves using many elf-sized tools, including the Peppermint Grappling Hook, Candy Cane Cable and Christmas Climbing Boots.

9

Sugar cookies are Santa's favourite biscuit (made to Mrs. Claus's secret recipe of course).

What's your REINDEER NAME?

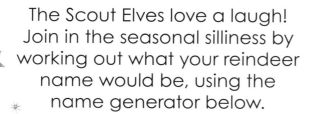

The Scout Elves love a laugh! Join in the seasonal silliness by working out what your reindeer name would be, using the name generator below.

HOW TO GENERATE YOUR NAME

Take the initial of your first name and the month you were born, then check what they stand for in the lists below. For example, if your name is Emily and you were born in July, your reindeer name is Lightning O'Flurry.

A = Gumdrop
B = Sugar
C = Blizzard
D = Dazzles
E = Lightning
F = Pecan
G = Patches
H = Peppermint
I = Admiral

J = Speedy
K = Mistletoe
L = Snuggles
M = Cinnamon
N = Chestnut
O = Spark
P = Jolly
Q = Sprinkles
R = Icy

S = Flash
T = Captain
U = Peppermint
V = Snowflake
W = Dizzy
X = Wiggles
Y = Bootsie
Z = Cocoa

January = McJingles
February = Frostington
March = Sleighski
April = Whiskerton
May = Twinkle Toes
June = Wonderland

July = O'Flurry
August = Gallopsalot
September = Brightstar
October = Hoofington
November = Slushbucket
December = Snugglewell

Name

Month of birth

Reindeer name

Christmas Changes

This creative Scout Elf has had fun with some googly eyes! Can you find eight differences in the picture on the right?

COLOUR A PRESENT EACH TIME YOU SPOT A DIFFERENCE.

Answers
on pages
76-77

37

Let it Snow!

Snow doubt about it, Christmas is coming! Make this magical snowflake picture to celebrate the season. It's bursting with Scout Elf sparkle!

YOU WILL NEED

- Scissors
- White PVA glue
- Salt
- Watercolour paint
- Small paintbrush

How to make

1
Carefully cut out the template on the opposite page.

2
Trace over the lines of the snowflakes with glue – you need to do this quickly so that the glue doesn't dry.

3
Pour salt over the glue snowflakes, making sure they're completely covered.

4
Tip the paper to shake off any excess salt.

5
Dip the paintbrush into the watercolour paint and gently dab it onto a salt snowflake so that the salt absorbs the colour.

6
Paint each snowflake then leave your picture to dry.

TOP TIP
You can use water and food colouring instead of watercolour paint.

38

Seasonal SNAPSHOTS

Can you put these pictures in the right order to document the Scout Elves' stay, from arriving to saying goodbye?

1 Arriving at their family's home.

2 Creating lots of fun hiding spots.

3 Flying back to the North Pole each night.

4 Saying goodbye until next year.

A

ANSWER

B

ANSWER

C

ANSWER

D

ANSWER

Answers on pages 76-77

MAKING Magic

The Scout Elves are sorting faith, hope and love from the Christmas Star so Santa can make magic. Which trails should they follow to find these three things?

Answers on pages 76-77

Christmas Colouring

These Scout Elves are busy preparing for the festive season. Use your brightest pens to add some Christmas cheer to the happy scene.

43

Ways to be Kind

Your Scout Elf flies back to the North Pole every evening to report your kind deeds to Santa. Here are some ideas of kind things you can do.

Share a treat with a friend.

Play with a school friend who's on their own.

Tell your mum or dad how much you love them.

Give a friend a hug if they're feeling sad.

Help set the table for dinner.

Make a card for a grandparent.

Surprise someone with a homemade gift.

Make your bed in the morning without being asked.

Share your toys when friends come to play.

Tidy your toys away at the end of the day.

KIND THINGS I'VE DONE TODAY

DID YOU KNOW?

Kindness creates Christmas spirit which Santa needs to make Christmas magic.

Spot the Scout Elves

These cheeky elves are hiding. Can you find them somewhere in the crowd?

Answers on pages 76-77

45

December

When your Scout Elf arrives,
every day is a new adventure!

MONDAY	TUESDAY	WEDNESDAY
	1	2
7	8	9 Which emoji sums up today's hiding place?
14 Where do you think your elf will be tomorrow?	15	16
21	22	23
28	29	30

2020

Use this calendar to record where your elf was hiding each day.

THURSDAY	FRIDAY	SATURDAY	SUNDAY
3	4 Give your elf an idea for where to hide tomorrow.	5	6
10	11	12	13
17	18	19 Does today's hiding spot get a thumbs up? 👍	20
24	25 How excited are you today? /10	26	27
31			

Wonderful Wrapping

Elves are expert wrappers and know how to make a present look perfect. Use these North Pole ideas to make the outside of your gifts as exciting as the inside!

YOU WILL NEED

- Parcel paper
- Scissors
- Sticky tape
- Paint in green, brown, white and black
- Other brightly coloured paint
- Paintbrush
- Black and orange felt-tip pens

HOW TO MAKE

Magical Reindeer

1. Lay out a piece of parcel paper.
2. Use brown paint to add a brown handprint to the paper.
3. Add eyes and a nose with finger paint to turn your handprint into a reindeer.

Terrific Trees

1. Cut a piece of parcel paper and lay it on a flat surface.
2. Use the paintbrush to paint one of your hands green and add a green handprint on the paper to make a Christmas tree.
3. Use your finger tips to paint baubles on the tree in your favourite bright colours.

Snow Family

1. Lay out a piece of parcel paper.
2. Make a white handprint on the paper and leave the paint to dry.
3. Turn your handprint into a snow family by using a black pen to draw on eyes and buttons, then adding carrot noses with an orange pen.

WARNING!
ADULT GUIDANCE IS NEEDED FOR THIS ACTIVITY.

TAG IT

Cut out these elf gift tags to put on your Christmas presents. They're snow cool!

YOU WILL NEED

- Scissors
- Hole punch
- Thin ribbon
- Ruler
- Sticky tape

HOW TO MAKE

1. Cut out the gift tag along the dotted lines.

2. Use a hole punch to make a hole where the white circle is.

3. Cut a 10cm length of ribbon, thread it through the hole and tie the ends together.

4. Write your gift tag and use sticky tape to attach it, by the ribbon, to your present.

Warm Winter Wishes

Keep it Merry!

From:

To:

To:

From:

To:

From:

To:

From:

Festive Fun

How quickly can you find the Scout Elves' favourite festive things in the wordsearch below? They're hidden vertically, horizontally, diagonally and backwards.

```
A G N I K C O T S K E
E P W M Q N S W R I K
H R E P L I G H T S A
E E S P B A U F L T L
L S S B P G T K F A F
B E A J E E K X S R W
U N E U A S R C O M O
A T D O I B R M T L N
B D C L I G D S I O S
K O S Q Y P S T H N L
C A N D Y C A N E B T
```

- [✓] BAUBLE
- [✓] CANDY CANE
- [✓] PRESENT

- [✓] LIGHTS
- [ ] PEPPERMINT
- [✓] SNOWFLAKE

- [✓] COCOA
- [✓] STOCKING
- [✓] STAR

Answers on pages 76-77

Know your Elf

Your elf's hiding spots reveal a lot about their personality. Tick the statements below that sound most like your elf to find out more about them.

They amaze me every day.

They make me laugh.

They often hide up high.

It's usually hard to find them.

I never know what they'll do next.

They create scenes from everyday objects.

They like to use props.

They're good at climbing.

They are a bit silly.

They choose daring hiding spots. ☐

They hide in funny places. ☐

They have a good imagination. ☐

They never hide in the same place twice. ☐

They like to play jokes. ☐

They are very inventive. ☐

MOSTLY BLUE

Your elf is creative! With a talent for making imaginative hiding places, your elf uses objects and props to surprise you every day.

CREATIVE

MOSTLY GREEN

You've got an adventurous elf! Brave and bold, your elf always finds the highest, hardest, most extreme places to hide.

ADVENTUROUS

MOSTLY RED

Your elf is playful! They love planning silly surprises and finding funny hiding spots to make the family smile.

PLAYFUL

A MIX OF COLOURS

Your multi-talented elf is a little bit of everything! You never know what they're going to do next to surprise and amaze you.

A MIXTURE

COOKIE *Creation*

Santa loves cookies of all kinds. Create and decorate your own festive treat for him below.

STEP 1   Pick a cookie.

CHOCOLATE CHIP   GINGER   CHOCOLATE

STEP 2   Choose your icing.

WHITE   GREEN   RED

STEP 3   Select a topping.

SPRINKLES   JELLY SWEETS   CHOCOLATE BEANS

STEP 4

Decorate your cookie.

Why not leave your cookie creation and note out for your Scout Elf to deliver to Santa in the North Pole?

Make sure you've read page 56 before you cut the cookie out. If you don't want to cut up your book, photocopy or scan and print this page instead.

WARNING!
ADULT GUIDANCE IS NEEDED FOR THIS ACTIVITY.

Dear Santa

I hope you like the cookie I've decorated for you.

It is a .... biscuit with ....

icing, topped with ....

I think it looks good enough to eat!

I'll leave a real treat out for you on Christmas Eve.

love from ....

WHO'S HIDING?

Santa's special helpers are enjoying the North Pole snow. Can you work out who is hiding behind each flurry of snowflakes?

1

2

3

4

Answers on pages 76-77

Festive Finds

Oh what fun, the Scout Elves have made a Christmas scavenger hunt for you! Can you find everything on the list around your home?

STOCKING

PRESENT

STAR

CHRISTMAS LIGHTS

BAUBLE

GINGERBREAD MAN

CANDLE

ADVENT CALENDAR

SNOWFLAKE

SWEET

CANDY CANE

MITTENS

SANTA HAT

CHRISTMAS TREE

HOLLY

SNOWMAN

SPOTTED!

Your Scout Elf loves to make you laugh with a cheeky hiding place. Leave some simple supplies out to help them have some fun!

Sprinkles Angel

You've heard of snow angels but have you ever seen a sprinkles angel? Leave some sugar sprinkles out for your elf and let them have some fun!

A Cosy Spot

Leave your sock drawer open and see if anything catches your elf's eye. Soft bed socks make the perfect elf sleeping bag!

SNOWBALL FUN

Who knew a piece of white paper could be so much fun? Leave one out for your elf and see if they use it for an indoor snowball fight like these elves have!

MOBILE MOVIE

Elves love watching films. Try leaving out a mobile phone and some toy cars to see if your elf can make their own drive-in movie theatre!

UNUSUAL TREE

This elf has decorated a milk bottle to look like a Christmas tree! Why not leave some green food colouring, ribbon and pompoms out and see if your elf does the same?

BALLOON BUBBLE BATH

A splash in the tub is just what an elf needs after flying back from the North Pole. Let your elf recreate this bubble bath in the sink with some small white balloons!

PLAYING GAMES

Coloured sticky tape is the perfect prop to leave for your inventive Scout Elf. Will they make a game of noughts and crosses like this elf has?

CANDY CANE GOLF

A candy cane makes the perfect elf-sized golf club! Leave one for your elf, along with a mini marshmallow, green paper and a pen, and let them do the rest!

MAGIC MARKER
MISCHIEF

Cheeky elves love being let loose with a marker pen! Leave one out for your elf and see what mischief they make!

Marshmallow Avalanche!

A paper cup slide is so much more fun when you have a soft landing! Would your elf like to recreate this sweet, squishy ride?

TREAT HUNT

Elves love to surprise their families with treats. This one has hidden something sweet under one of the paper cups. Your elf might like to do the same.

SEASONAL SEQUENCES

Oh what fun, the Scout Elves have a festive puzzle for you to complete! Can you work out which Christmas item is missing from each sequence?

Answers on pages 76-77

Candy COUNT

Peppermints are the Scout Elves' favourite Christmas candy. How many minty sweets can you count in the jar below?

Here I am

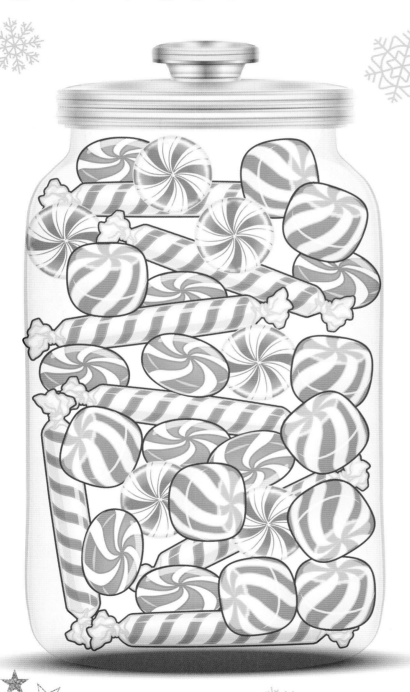

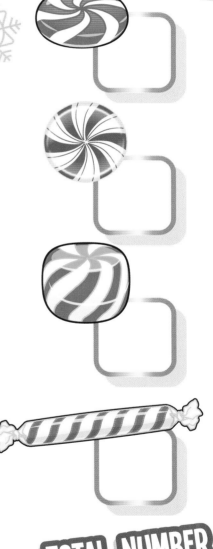

TOTAL NUMBER OF SWEETS

Answers on pages 76-77

Strawberry SANTA HATS

These Santa-inspired sweet treats are super easy to make. Don't forget to save one for your Scout Elf to take to the North Pole!

YOU WILL NEED

- Ready-made mini chocolate brownies
- Double cream or squirty cream
- Strawberries

WARNING!
ADULT GUIDANCE IS NEEDED FOR THIS ACTIVITY.

HOW TO MAKE

1. Wash the strawberries and cut off the green end.

2. If you're using double cream, whisk it until it stands in peaks.

3. Squirt or pipe a circle of cream around the top of each chocolate brownie.

4. Place a strawberry upside down on top of the cream to make a Santa hat.

5. Squirt or pipe a small amount of cream on to the end of each strawberry to make the hat's pompom. Your tasty treats are now ready to enjoy.

TOP TIP
You could use white icing instead of cream if you prefer.

ELF DELIVERY!

Why not send a strawberry hat to the North Pole for Santa to enjoy? Just leave one out for your elf to deliver with the note below.

Make sure you've read page 66 before you cut the template out. If you don't want to cut up your book, photocopy or scan and print this page instead.

Dear Santa

I made these delicious strawberry Santa hats and thought you might like to try one!

I'm sending it to you by Elf Express, delivered by my very own Scout Elf ....

I hope you like it!

love from ....

ELF ALERT!

Scout Elves are specially trained to find the best hiding places. Can you spot 10 elves hidden in this room?

COLOUR A CANDY CANE EACH TIME YOU SPOT AN ELF.

Answers on pages 76-77

67

Christmas
AROUND THE WORLD

Well-travelled Scout Elves know all about Christmas traditions around the world. Find out more about some of their favourites.

SWEET TREAT

Sweet-toothed elves love the Mexican tradition of piñata at Christmas time. People take it in turns to hit the piñata with a stick until it splits open and the treats hidden inside fall to the floor.

NICE NOËL

Christmas in France is called Noël. The main Christmas meal is eaten on Christmas Eve or very early on Christmas morning after families have returned from a midnight church service.

SKATING FUN

In Caracas, the capital of Venezuela, it's tradition to roller skate to church on Christmas Day! Roads are often closed to traffic to make room for the skaters.

LUCKY WEBS

People in Ukraine decorate their Christmas trees with fake spiders' webs. It is believed that the webs will bring good luck for the coming year.

SPECIAL DELIVERY

In the UK, it used to be tradition for children to throw their letters to Santa into the fireplace. The letters would float up the chimney and be delivered to Santa in the North Pole.

FUN IN THE SUN

While most people think of Christmas as cold and wintry, in Australia Christmas falls in the middle of summer. Many Australians spend the day on the beach having a BBQ!

CHRISTMAS GIFTS

In Norway children open their presents on Christmas Eve rather than on Christmas Day. They are placed under the Christmas tree and unwrapped after dinner.

LONG CELEBRATION

If you love Christmas, you should consider moving to the Philippines! The Christmas season there starts in September and doesn't end until January!

SLEIGH DASH

This Scout Elf is in a hurry to help Santa load his sleigh. Can you help by using the instructions to guide him to the present?

HOW TO MOVE

GO DOWN · GO LEFT · GO RIGHT

START

FINISH

Answers on pages 76-77

GET CREATIVE

Santa will soon be on his way to fill your Christmas stocking with surprises! While you wait, decorate this stocking with a fun, festive design.

WRITE YOUR NAME HERE.

Decorate this elf-sized stocking for your North Pole visitor!

DECORATION IDEAS

7

Christmas ROUND-UP

On Christmas Eve, Scout Elves return to the North Pole. Before your elf friend flies back, fill in these pages to remember all the festive fun you had.

Draw a picture of your elf or stick a photo of them here.

My Scout Elf is called

....

THIS YEAR, MY ELF'S FAVOURITE HIDING SPOT WAS:

THE FUNNIEST PLACE THEY HID WAS:

The hardest place to find my elf was:

The most creative thing they did was:

The words that best describe December with my elf are:

- ☐ FUN
- ☐ EXCITING
- ☐ INTERESTING
- ☐ AMAZING
- ☐ UNPREDICTABLE
- ☐ HILARIOUS

Some of the props my elf used were:

DID YOU KNOW?
Scout Elves start preparing for next year's Christmas on December 26th.

IN THE NORTH POLE

Christmas may only come once a year but hard-working Scout Elves are busy all year round. Let's find out more about some of their important jobs.

☑ SPECIAL PROJECTS

The North Pole is always undergoing upgrades and sometimes Santa assigns his elves a special North Pole project. It might be building an igloo, renovating the Grotto or adding new gadgets to his sleigh.

ICE ICE BABY!

☑ ANIMAL FRIENDS

Santa's trusted reindeer, who live in the stables at the North Pole, are looked after by Scout Elves. They feed them, keep their stables warm and cosy and play fun games together.

KEEPING IN TOUCH

Santa receives letters from children all year round, not just at Christmas. Scout Elves work hard in the Mail Room to organise and sort the post for Santa. Sometimes they even write replies.

Dear Santa,

Please bring a doll for my little sister.

I know it will make her very happy.

Love,
Jackson

 # TRAINING TIME

In order to keep up-to-date with the latest tips and tricks, elves must pass Scout Elf Training Camp. Learning to jump higher, climb faster and freeze in one place for longer keeps them fit and busy.

 # PLANNING AHEAD

Whenever they have a spare moment, creative elves are keen to brush up on their arts and crafts skills. They swap ideas and plan fun and innovative hiding places for next season.

DID YOU KNOW?
Elves are very sociable and love spending time with their friends.

ANSWERS

PAGE 5
Hidden Scout elves

 20  19

There are more girl Scout Elves hiding.

PAGES 8-9
Special Delivery

PAGES 18-19
FabYULEous Fun!

1. SNOW DOUBT ABOUT IT, CHRISTMAS IS HERE!

2. BELIEVE IN YOUR ELF!

3. WE RUN ON CHRISTMAS SPIRIT!

4. NEVER NAUGHTY, ALWAYS NICE!

PAGE 22
Christmas Close-ups

 1 Bauble
 2 Candy cane
 3 Present

 4 Hot chocolate
 5 Holly
 6 Snowman

PAGES 36-37
Christmas Changes

PAGE 40
Seasonal Snapshots

1 – C, 2 – B, 3 – A, 4 – D.

PAGE 41
Making Magic

The Scout Elves should follow trails B, D and E.

PAGE 45
Spot the Scout Elves

PAGE 51
Festive Fun

PAGE 56
Who's Hiding?

PAGE 62
Seasonal Sequences

PAGE 63
Candy Count

PAGES 66-67
ELF ALERT!

PAGE 70
Sleigh Dash